THE HINDENBURG DISASTER

BY CHRIS BOWMAN

ILLUSTRATION BY BRENT SCHOONOVER

COLOR BY GERARDO SANDOVAL

BELLWETHER MEDIA · MINNEAPOLIS, MN

STRAY FROM REGULAR READS WITH BLACK SHEEP BOOKS. FEEL A RUSH WITH EVERY READ!

Library of Congress Cataloging-in-Publication Data

Bowman, Chris, 1990-
  The Hindenburg Disaster / by Chris Bowman.
      pages cm. -- (Black Sheep: Disaster Stories)
  Includes bibliographical references and index.
  Summary: "Exciting illustrations follow the events of the Hindenburg disaster. The combination of brightly colored panels and leveled text is intended for students in grades 3 through 7"-- Provided by publisher.
  ISBN 978-1-62617-153-4 (hardcover : alk. paper)
  1. Hindenburg (Airship)--Comic books, strips, etc. 2. Hindenburg (Airship)--Juvenile literature. 3. Aircraft accidents--New Jersey--Comic books, strips, etc. 4. Aircraft accidents--New Jersey--Juvenile literature. 5. Airships--Germany--Comic books, strips, etc. 6. Airships--Germany--Juvenile literature. I. Title.
  TL659.H5B69 2014
  363.12'492--dc23
                                    2014009046

This edition first published in 2015 by Bellwether Media, Inc.

Printed in the United States of America, North Mankato, MN.

TABLE OF CONTENTS

Orange text identifies historical quotes.

May 3, 1937:
The **airship** LZ 129 *Hindenburg* is set for its first flight of the year from Frankfurt, Germany to Lakehurst, New Jersey. This trip was made ten times the year before.

The *Hindenburg* is amazing. It's so big!

It's 804 feet long. They say it's the biggest in the world!

How does it fly?

It's filled with hydrogen, so it floats like a balloon.

At the time, airships were the standard of **luxury travel** for the upper class. Passengers enjoyed good food in big dining rooms. They relaxed in lounges and **promenades**.

Airships traveled from Europe to America faster than **steamships**. They could make the trip in just a couple days.

Won't it pop?

Oh, don't say that!

Captain Pruss! Good to see you again.

I'm excited to be back in the air again. And we have such a skilled crew on board!

Of course it won't. It has a huge frame made of aluminum. Airships are as safe as can be.

Six captains are on board the *Hindenburg*. Commanding Officer Max Pruss is in charge.

Mr. Späh, we've told you before that you are not allowed back here alone.

I just wanted to make sure Ulla was being cared for.

You must ask a steward to go with you when you want to check on her.

I will, sir. My apologies.

The *Hindenburg* then flies over southern Greenland. Next, it reaches North America at the Canadian **province** of Newfoundland.

Looks like a storm is coming. Captain Lehmann, is there any danger of being struck by lightning?

None, Mr. Späh. Don't worry. We are safe.

The *Hindenburg* is scheduled to arrive at Lakehurst on May 6 at 6:00 a.m. However, the heavy winds delay its arrival by several hours.

We are hitting strong **headwinds**.

Are we in danger?

No, but we will be behind schedule.

May 6, 1937, 3:00 p.m.
The *Hindenburg* reaches New York City.

What building is that?

It's the Empire State Building!

It's so big!

Now aren't you glad we took the *Hindenburg* and saved two days? We might still be at sea.

I'll be glad when we're on the ground.

However, the *Hindenburg's* landing is pushed back even more.

Weather report from Commander Rosendahl at Lakehurst Naval Air Station, sir. Heavy storms with winds reaching 25 **knots**. They recommend we delay landing.

We will be there a bit after 4:00 p.m. We will just have to circle until the weather clears.

DISASTER STRIKES!

It's fire—and it's crashing! It's crashing terrible! Oh, my, get out of the way, please! It's burning and bursting into flames...

Many members of the landing crew immediately run toward the *Hindenburg* to help survivors.

Navy men, stand fast!

...it's just laying there, a mass of smoking **wreckage**. Ah! And everybody can hardly breathe and talk, and the screaming...

Nearby vehicles help take survivors away from the wreckage.

Hermann, Irene, and 33 others did not survive the 34-second crash.

Nobody knows what started the fire. One **theory** is that static electricity sparked the hydrogen supply.

Oh the humanity!

Another theory is that the *Hindenburg* got struck by lightning. Some people even think there was a bomb on board.

No matter the cause, the disaster marked the end of airships. The videos, photographs, and radio broadcasts spread fear. Passenger airplanes took off in 1939.

MORE ABOUT THE DISASTER

- Airships were also known as *dirigibles* or *zeppelins*.

- Throughout 1936, the *Hindenburg* had a baby grand piano in one of the lounges. It was made of aluminum to keep it light. It was taken out before 1937 to save weight.

- The *Hindenburg* was carrying about 17,000 letters on its trip to the U.S. About 170 of these survived the crash and were delivered.

- Herbert Morrison's report of the *Hindenburg* disaster was not broadcast live on the radio. The recording was played the next day.

- Instead of hydrogen, the *Hindenburg* was designed to use helium, which was less capable of catching fire. However, the U.S. controlled the world's helium supply. They did not sell any to Germany out of fear that it would be used for military purposes.

Glossary

airship—a large aircraft filled with a lighter-than-air gas

altitude—the height above ground

ballast water—water kept in an airship to keep it stable and control its height

catastrophes—sudden disasters or tragedies

headwinds—winds blowing against the direction of travel

knots—a way to measure the speed of aircraft and ships; a knot is equal to one nautical mile, or 1.15 miles (1.85 kilometers).

luxury travel—comfortable ways for the upper class to move from place to place

mooring lines—ropes used to keep an airship in place; workers used mooring lines to help airships land.

mooring mast—a structure that airships use to land; airships dock at mooring masts.

promenades—open areas with windows for passengers to look out

province—an area within a country; provinces are similar to states.

steamships—ships powered by a steam engine

theory—an idea that tries to explain something

wreckage—the remains of something that has been badly damaged or destroyed

To Learn More

AT THE LIBRARY

Berne, Emma Carlson. *The Rescue Adventure of Stenny Green, Hindenburg Crash Eyewitness*. Minneapolis, Minn.: Graphic Universe, 2011.

Doeden, Matt. *The Hindenburg Disaster*. Mankato, Minn.: Capstone Press, 2006.

Gunderson, Jessica. *Fire in the Sky: A Tale of the Hindenburg Explosion*. Mankato, Minn.: Stone Arch Books, 2009.

ON THE WEB

Learning more about the *Hindenburg* disaster is as easy as 1, 2, 3.

1. Go to www.factsurfer.com.
2. Enter "Hindenburg disaster" into the search box.
3. Click the "Surf" button and you will see a list of related web sites.

With factsurfer.com, finding more information is just a click away.

Index